One-Minute Challenges 2000

Math & English

by Susan Shafer
and Linda Aber

Troll

This edition printed in 1998.

Printed in the United States of America.

10 9 8 7 6 5 4 3 2 1

INTRODUCTION

What a great way to help your students boost their math and language skills! This useful book is packed with fun and challenging one-minute tests to help kids learn.

The first half of the book, which begins on page 5, is filled with a wide variety of math puzzles and problems. The one-minute English exercises start on page 45. The answers to all the tests begin on page 85.

Sharpening your students' math and language skills was never so much fun—or so easy!

ONE-MINUTE
MATH
CHALLENGES

ADD IT!

Add.

1. 431
    +247

6. 538
    +211

2. 273
    +701

7. 628
    +370

3. 584
    +415

8. 404
    +574

4. 605
    +393

9. 148
    +721

5. 377
    +420

10. 336
    +633

BONUS ROUND!

If you finished all the problems in less than a minute, try adding these.

625	777	975	461
+ 331	+ 121	+ 214	+ 804

CAN YOU ADD THESE?

You'll need all your addition skills to do these problems. Can you solve all of them in a minute?

1. 63,306
   + 23,682

2. 456,602
   + 223,106

3. 22,154
   + 46,334

4. 123,454
   + 542,524

5. 28,705
   + 11,243

6. 777,666
   + 201,212

7. 43,702
   + 43,065

8. 664,123
   + 224,233

9. 303,541
   + 582,042

10. 11,603
    + 35,023

BONUS ROUND!

If you finished these problems in less than a minute, you're an addition champ! Now try these for extra practice.

333,672
+ 704,113

124,689
+ 52,110

94,364
+ 82,111

74,999
+ 23,000

Add Numbers with Exchange

You will need to use regrouping (exchange) in these problems. See if you can complete these in 60 seconds or less!

1. 4,367
   + 4,434

2. 1,246
   + 3,345

3. 2,390
   + 6,523

4. 6,763
   + 1,144

5. 35,547
   + 36,345

6. 81,054
   + 11,856

7. 71,903
   + 11,276

8. 66,225
   + 23,456

BONUS ROUND!

62,445	8,990	1,259	7,779
+ 12,607	+ 2,541	+ 4,667	+ 6,248

COLUMN ADDITION

Add these columns of numbers. You will need to regroup.

1. 16
    25
    10
  + 41

2. 25
    32
    15
  + 40

3. 44
    11
    26
  + 34

4. 36
    33
    23
  + 15

5. 321
    480
  + 269

6. 329
    345
  + 473

7. 7,745
    1,234
  + 4,452

8. 1,002
    7,876
  + 3,345

BONUS ROUND!

Find all your answers in the number search puzzle. Look up, down, across, and diagonally. Can you find them all in less than a minute?

```
1  6  4  2  4  9  7  6  4
1  0  0  4  3  1  6  2  5
5  0  6  4  4  1  1  1  0
4  2  7  3  8  5  0  1  1
3  8  9  1  9  7  0  7  3
0  3  6  9  0  3  4  6  4
7  4  1  1  0  6  1  4  3
1  5  9  4  3  2  2  2  1
```

Read and Add

Solve these word problems.

1. In the Jefferson School District, there are 755 students in the Adler School, 1,345 students in the Smith School, and 2,795 students in the Bosco School. What is the total student population of the three schools? _____

2. 4,459 people attended the Spring Fair on Friday, 998 people attended on Saturday, and 774 people attended on Sunday. How many people attended the three-day event? _____

3. A sneaker manufacturer was distributing free sneakers to community centers in Washingtonville. During the first week 2,364 pairs were given away. During the second week, they gave out 594 pairs. In the third week, they gave out 25,540 pairs. How many pairs did the manufacturer give out in all? _____

SUBTRACT!

Subtract to find the answers.

1. 6,856	2. 6,789	3. 7,588	4. 5,377
- 4,706	- 5,555	- 7,153	- 3,257

5. 9,987	6. 7,642	7. 3,663	8. 2,456
- 5,436	- 6,530	- 2,251	- 1,345

9. 4,436	10. 6,702	11. 8,098	12. 5,568
- 3,234	- 5,501	- 3,077	- 1,123

13. 5,462	14. 2,345
- 2,262	- 2,023

SUBTRACT AGAIN!

Subtract to find these answers. Set your timer for one minute!

1. 200	2. 600	3. 4,000	4. 3,000
- 175	- 448	- 3,602	- 1,198

5. 500	6. 700	7. 7,000
- 426	- 550	- 4,422

BONUS ROUND!

If you solved all the problems in less than a minute, try these brainbusters!

9,241	4,632	391	6,299
- 6,311	- 988	- 78	- 4,986

Subtraction Word Problems

Take a minute to solve these problems. Use the space after each problem to work your answer.

1. Jennifer is taking a plane trip of 5,000 miles. She has already traveled 2,378 miles. How many more miles does she have to go? _____

2. The A+ Grocery Store planned to give away 2,000 bananas to the local community. They have already handed out 1,447. How many more bananas will they give away?_____

3. The Tasty Bake Shop made 3,000 doughnuts for a party. They put sprinkles on 2,261. If they want all the doughnuts to have sprinkles, how many more do they have to go?_____

4. John, a rock climber, climbed 1,567 feet of a 3,000-foot mountain. How many more feet must he climb to reach the top?_____

BONUS ROUND!

If you have extra time, try this brain teaser.

The Mega Music Store bought 9,000 copies of the new Blue Moon CD. In one day, 3,692 copies were sold. How many copies of the CD does the store have left? _____

MULTIPLICATION MEDLEY

Take a minute to master this multiplication challenge.

1. 10
   x 2

2. 40
   x 5

3. 70
   x 7

4. 50
   x 3

5. 300
   x 2

6. 900
   x 4

7. 600
   x 7

8. 800
   x 6

9. 21
   x 4

10. 23
    x 3

11. 42
    x 4

12. 71
    x 3

13. 422
    x 3

14. 325
    x 4

MORE MULTIPLICATION

These problems are a bit more tricky. Remember to regroup
if you have to.

1. 53
  x 34

2. 64
  x 25

3. 44
  x 23

4. 63
  x 29

5. 74
  x 32

6. 45
  x 74

7. 29
  x 81

8. 17
  x 65

9. 27
  x 94

10. 33
   x 66

Divide and Conquer

Take this division challenge. See how many problems you can finish in a minute. Remember to regroup if necessary.

1. $2\overline{)15}$ 2. $2\overline{)49}$ 3. $8\overline{)75}$

4. $4\overline{)66}$ 5. $3\overline{)653}$ 6. $7\overline{)908}$

7. $6\overline{)783}$ 8. $5\overline{)511}$ 9. $4\overline{)337}$

10. $6\overline{)581}$

More Than, Less Than, or Equal To?

Compare the decimals. Then decide whether the first decimal is greater than (>), less than (<), or equal to (=) the second. Can you finish these problems in one minute?

1. 0.41 ___ 0.56

2. 2.6 ___ 2.38

3. 9.1 ___ 9.1

4. 3.61 ___ 3.08

5. 0.75 ___ 0.57

6. 3.11 ___ 1.31

7. 4.50 ___ 4.5

8. 8.91 ___ 1.89

9. .06 ___ .09

10. 4.95 ___ 3.98

11. 6.5 ___ 7.0

12. 0.7 ___ .7

13. 4.3 ___ 4.27

14. 7.07 ___ .77

15. 5.55 ___ 5.99

16. .68 ___ 1.54

Above Average!

Find the mean, or average, of each set of numbers. To find the mean, add all the numbers in each set, then divide the answer by the number of items in each set.

1. 125
    247
    + 162

2. 472
    378
    + 485

3. $664
    $755
    + $708

4. 476
    467
    983
    + 474

5. 326
    164
    138
    + 276

6. 520
    776
    332
    + 600

THAT'S IMPROPER!

Change each improper fraction to a mixed number or a whole number. How many can you finish in a minute?

1. $\frac{6}{5}$ _____

2. $\frac{7}{5}$ _____

3. $\frac{8}{4}$ _____

4. $\frac{9}{4}$ _____

5. $\frac{6}{3}$ _____

6. $\frac{7}{4}$ _____

7. $\frac{10}{5}$ _____

8. $\frac{8}{3}$ _____

9. $\frac{5}{2}$ _____

10. $\frac{7}{3}$ _____

11. $\frac{12}{7}$ _____

12. $\frac{11}{4}$ _____

13. $\frac{15}{7}$ _____

14. $\frac{13}{5}$ _____

15. $\frac{16}{7}$ _____

16. $\frac{14}{3}$ _____

Roman Numerals

You've got one minute to write the Roman numeral for each of the following numbers.

1. 5   _____

2. 10   _____

3. 100   _____

4. 50   _____

5. 60   _____

6. 70   _____

7. 80   _____

8. 151   _____

9. 293   _____

10. 399   _____

MORE ROMAN NUMERALS

Change these Roman numerals to Arabic numbers in one minute or less!

1. CCC _____

2. CD _____

3. D _____

4. M _____

5. MM _____

6. MXVI _____

7. MCCCXXII _____

8. DXXVII _____

9. MCXXII _____

10. MCCCXXIII _____

SPECIAL SEVENS

Look at each number. Decide if the digit 7 is in the ones, tens, hundreds, thousands, ten thousands, hundred thousands, or millions place. Write your answer on the line next to each problem.

1. 7,539,021 _____

2. 5,093,471 _____

3. 6,980,752 _____

4. 9,720,106 _____

5. 4,579,236 _____

6. 3,657,859 _____

7. 2,625,947 _____

8. 1,567,618 _____

9. 9,064,072 _____

10. 7,964,906 _____

11. 6,702,513 _____

12. 5,978,310 _____

13. 2,642,871 _____

14. 6,107,346 _____

15. 2,404,167 _____

FRACTION ACTION

Change each mixed number to an improper fraction.

1. $2\frac{3}{4}$ _____

2. $4\frac{1}{2}$ _____

3. $3\frac{2}{3}$ _____

4. $5\frac{7}{8}$ _____

5. $1\frac{3}{4}$ _____

6. $2\frac{3}{5}$ _____

7. $1\frac{1}{3}$ _____

8. $6\frac{5}{6}$ _____

9. $8\frac{4}{5}$ _____

10. $7\frac{7}{12}$ _____

BONUS ROUND!
Try these problems if you finish in less than a minute.

$9\frac{7}{8}$ _____ $12\frac{1}{2}$ _____ $6\frac{2}{3}$ _____

$4\frac{8}{9}$ _____ $11\frac{11}{12}$ _____

DIVISION STUMPERS

Take the division challenge! *Hint*: Answers will have
remainders.

1. 3⟌7805   2. 5⟌2561   3. 7⟌7046

4. 4⟌3582   5. 5⟌3716

WHAT IS THE RANGE? WHAT IS THE MEAN?

Find the range and the mean for each set of data.
Remember: The range is the difference between the highest
and the lowest numbers in a set.

1. Money Earned by Maria

Sunday	$45
Monday	$55
Tuesday	$80
Wednesday	$45
Thursday	$75
Friday	$80
Saturday	$75

Range = _____
Mean = _____

2. Temperature Lows

Sunday	24 degrees
Monday	34 degrees
Tuesday	25 degrees
Wednesday	30 degrees
Thursday	29 degrees
Friday	32 degrees
Saturday	43 degrees

Range = _____
Mean = _____

BONUS ROUND!

Find the range and mean for this data if you have extra time.

Math Test Scores

Lisa	89
Jay	76
Tom	91
Amanda	88
Mike	95
Sam	82
Amber	95

Range = _____
Mean = _____

ADDING MIXED NUMBERS

Add each set of mixed numbers. Express the sum in lowest terms. Set your timer for one minute!

1. $4\frac{1}{4}$
   $+2\frac{1}{4}$

4. $1\frac{5}{6}$
   $+7\frac{1}{2}$

2. $3\frac{3}{5}$
   $+2\frac{1}{4}$

5. $5\frac{1}{7}$
   $+6\frac{1}{4}$

3. $6\frac{1}{8}$
   $+2\frac{4}{9}$

6. $9\frac{2}{3}$
   $+3\frac{4}{5}$

SUBTRACTING MIXED NUMBERS

You have one minute to subtract these mixed numbers.
Express each difference in lowest terms.

1. $10\frac{5}{12}$
   $-\ 4\frac{1}{12}$

5. $6\frac{2}{3}$
   $-\ 3\frac{1}{8}$

2. $8\frac{2}{3}$
   $-\ 4\frac{2}{5}$

6. $7\frac{4}{5}$
   $-\ 2\frac{3}{4}$

3. $7\frac{3}{5}$
   $-\ 3\frac{1}{4}$

7. $9\frac{1}{2}$
   $-\ 4\frac{2}{5}$

4. $9\frac{4}{5}$
   $-\ 4\frac{1}{2}$

8. $8\frac{6}{7}$
   $-\ 2\frac{1}{4}$

MULTIPLY IT!

Multiply each number by the fraction. Then reduce the answer to lowest terms.

1. $11 \times \frac{1}{3} =$

2. $5 \times \frac{2}{5} =$

3. $12 \times \frac{1}{2} =$

4. $3 \times \frac{3}{5} =$

5. $3 \times \frac{4}{5} =$

BONUS ROUND!

If you have extra time, try these problems.

$9 \times \frac{2}{3} =$

$6 \times \frac{4}{9} =$

$4 \times \frac{3}{8} =$

READING GRAPHS AND CHARTS

In one minute or less, answer the questions based on the graph.

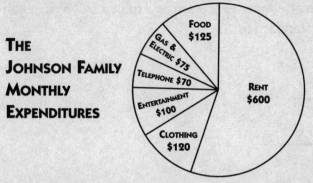

THE JOHNSON FAMILY MONTHLY EXPENDITURES

FOOD $125

GAS & ELECTRIC $75

TELEPHONE $70

ENTERTAINMENT $100

CLOTHING $120

RENT $600

1. How much more money is spent on food than on clothing? _____

2. What is the family's combined expenditure for gas/electric and telephone? _____

3. If the family cut its entertainment costs in half, how much would be saved every month? _____

Look at the chart below and answer these questions.

Beth, Allison, Courtney, and Tyesha swam in the 100-meter dash.

	Time in Seconds
Beth	55
Allison	58
Courtney	49
Tyesha	51

4. Which runner completed the event in the shortest time?_____
5. What is the difference in time between the fastest runner and the slowest? _____

Introducing Exponents

The numbers here are expressed as exponents. Write each number in standard form.

1. $4^3 =$ _____

2. $7^1 =$ _____

3. $3^4 =$ _____

4. $5^5 =$ _____

5. $8^0 =$ _____

6. $9^2 =$ _____

7. $10^3 =$ _____

8. $2^5 =$ _____

9. $6^4 =$ _____

10. $8^2 =$ _____

EXPONENT ALERT!

Write the exponent in the box for each problem below. How many can you do in a minute?

1. $5 \times 5 \times 5 \times 5 \times 5 = 5^{\boxed{}}$

2. $4 \times 4 \times 4 = 4^{\boxed{}}$

3. $9 \times 9 \times 9 \times 9 \times 9 \times 9 \times 9 = 9^{\boxed{}}$

4. $7 \times 7 \times 7 \times 7 \times 7 = 7^{\boxed{}}$

5. $6 \times 6 \times 6 = 6^{\boxed{}}$

6. $2 \times 2 = 2^{\boxed{}}$

7. $4 = 4^{\boxed{}}$

8. $3 \times 3 \times 3 \times 3 \times 3 = 3^{\boxed{}}$

9. $8 \times 8 = 8^{\boxed{}}$

10. $7 \times 7 \times 7 \times 7 = 7^{\boxed{}}$

11. $11 \times 11 \times 11 \times 11 \times 11 \times 11 = 11^{\boxed{}}$

12. $19 \times 19 = 19^{\boxed{}}$

13. $23 = 23^{\boxed{}}$

14. $5 \times 5 \times 5 \times 5 \times 5 \times 5 \times 5 = 5^{\boxed{}}$

15. $2 \times 2 \times 2 \times 2 \times 2 = 2^{\boxed{}}$

MULTIPLICATION CHALLENGE

Solve each problem by multiplying the 3-digit number by the 2-digit number. You'll be finished in a minute!

1. The Calico Computer Company shipped 223 new computers to its distributors for each of 12 months of the year. How many computers were shipped altogether? _____

2. Berkshire Farm Company sent 315 bushels of tomatoes to the city every month for 11 months. How many bushels did it ship during that period? _____

3. Over a 12-week period, the Delicious Bakery Company made 412 doughnuts each week. How many doughnuts did it make in all? _____

4. Some 125 students in the New Lebanon School District won science awards for each of the past 32 years. How many students have won the award altogether? _____

5. Susan put 414 cents in her piggy bank each day for 30 days. How much money has she saved in all? _____

PERIMETER

Find the perimeter of these shapes. (Hint: The perimeter is the sum of all the sides of an object.)

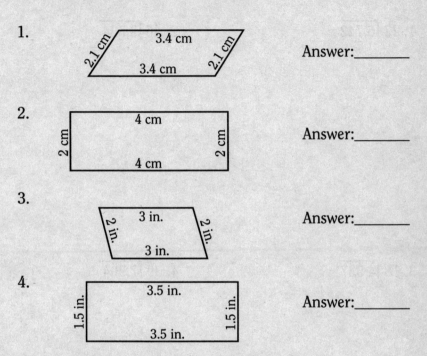

1.

3.4 cm

2.1 cm

2.1 cm

3.4 cm

Answer:_____

2.

4 cm

2 cm

2 cm

4 cm

Answer:_____

3.

3 in.

2 in.

2 in.

3 in.

Answer:_____

4.

3.5 in.

1.5 in.

1.5 in.

3.5 in.

Answer:_____

Find the answers to these problems.

5. A farmer wants to buy a fence for a field that is 55 feet wide and 34 feet long. How much fencing does the farmer need to buy?_____

6. An artist produced a painting that is 9.4 feet high and 4.6 feet wide. How much framing should she buy? _____

Divide Away!

Find the answers to these problems in one minute or less!

1. 23 $\overline{)6,742}$

2. 46 $\overline{)9,534}$

3. 18 $\overline{)4,537}$

4. 39 $\overline{)7,904}$

COORDINATE GEOMETRY

Write the coordinates for each point.

1. A _____

2. B _____

3. C _____

4. D _____

5. E _____

6. F _____

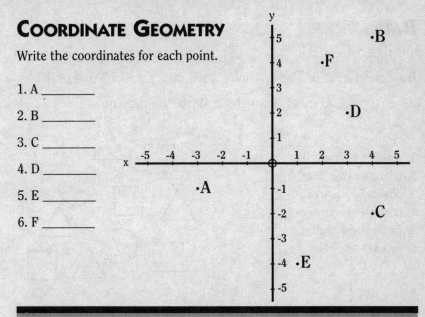

BONUS ROUND!

Look at the coordinates. Write the letter for each pair of coordinates on the lines below to find a hidden message.

7. (-5, +2)
8. (+4, +4)
9. (+2, -3)
10. (+5, -2)
11. (-2, -5)
12. (+1, +3)
13. (-4, -1)
14. (-5, -2)
15. (+5, -4)

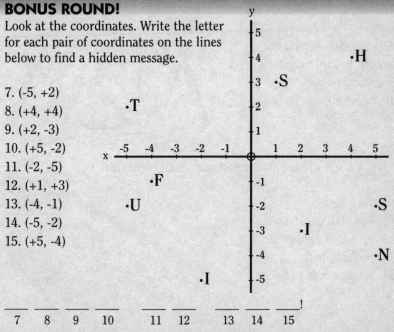

___ ___ ___ ___   ___ ___   ___ ___!
7   8   9   10   11   12   13   14   15

RATIO

A ratio is a comparison of two quantities. You can express a fraction as a ratio. For example, $\frac{3}{4}$ means a ratio of 3 to 4 or 3:4.

Look at the picture. Write the ratio of:

1. squares to triangles _____
2. triangles to circles _____
3. circles to squares _____
4. triangles to squares _____
5. circles to triangles _____
6. squares to circles _____

Look at the picture. Write the ratio of:

7. paper clips to erasers _____
8. pens to paper clips _____
9. erasers to pens _____
10. paper clips to pens _____

Look at the picture. Write the ratio of:

11. baseball bats to books _____
12. balls to baseball bats _____
13. books to balls _____
14. baseball bats to balls _____

36

Ratios and Proportions

Find the missing term in each proportion.

1. $\dfrac{1}{4} = \dfrac{5}{}$

2. $\dfrac{2}{3} = \dfrac{4}{}$

3. $\dfrac{3}{4} = \dfrac{6}{}$

4. $\dfrac{2}{5} = \dfrac{}{10}$

5. $\dfrac{4}{6} = \dfrac{2}{}$

6. $\dfrac{3}{6} = \dfrac{6}{}$

7. $\dfrac{4}{20} = \dfrac{}{5}$

Find the answer to each problem.

8. Maddy wanted to buy raffle tickets for a drawing at her club. If one ticket costs $4, how much would six tickets cost? _____

9. Robert wandered into a book fair. He saw that five old comic books were available for $1. How much would 15 comic books cost? _____

10. Michelle took a one-minute math test. If she completed 20 examples in 30 seconds, how many examples could she complete in 60 seconds? _____

A PART OF THE WHOLE

Look at the picture below. Write a fraction, a decimal, and a percent for the shaded areas.

1. Fraction _____
   Decimal _____
   Percent _____

2. An art exhibit showed 100 works of local artists. 75 were oil paintings. The rest were charcoals.
Express the number of charcoals as a fraction. _____
Express the number of charcoals as a decimal. _____
Express the number of charcoals as a percent. _____

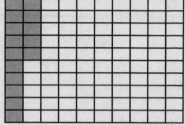

3. Marie read 100 books one summer. 35 were fiction. The rest were nonfiction.
Express the number of fiction books she read as a fraction. _____
Express the number of fiction books she read as a decimal. _____
Express the number of fiction books she read as a percent. _____

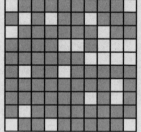

MULTIPLYING DECIMALS

Multiply these decimals in one minute or less. Remember to place the decimal point correctly in your answer.

1.   13.45
    x 5.9

2.   7.5
    x 4.3

3.   7.053
    x 3.5

BONUS ROUND!

Try one more!   24.624
                   x 32.5

DIVIDING DECIMALS

Divide these decimals in one minute or less. Remember to place the decimal point correctly in your answer.

1. .8)‾53.6‾   2. .03)‾65.1‾

3. 9.1)‾421.33‾

BONUS ROUND!
Time for one more?

.4)‾343.32‾

COMPARING FRACTIONS

Arrange these sets of fractions in order from the smallest to the largest. You will have to find common denominators to do this.

1. 3/5   9/10   1/4   _____

2. 1/2   3/8   5/6   _____

NAME THAT TRIANGLE

Look at the three triangles below. For each, write if it is a right triangle, an acute triangle, or an obtuse triangle.

1.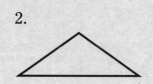

2.

3.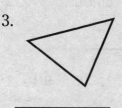

_____   _____   _____

Look at the length of the sides of the triangles below. For each, write if the triangle is equilateral, isosceles, or scalene.

4.

5.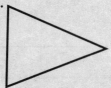

6.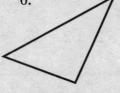

_____   _____   _____

BONUS ROUND!
Answer these questions if you have extra time.
The angles of a triangle always add up to 180°. Find the third angle for each triangle below.

100°, 30°, _____

40°, 60°, _____

90°, 45°, _____

33°, 115°, _____

Graphing Ordered Pairs

Match each ordered pair with the letter on the grid that shows its point.

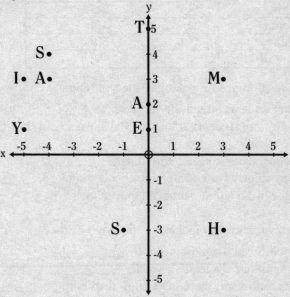

1. (3, 3) _____
2. (-4, 3) _____
3. (0, 5) _____
4. (3, -3) _____
5. (-5, 3) _____

6. (-4, 4) _____
7. (0, 1) _____
8. (0, 2) _____
9. (-1, -3) _____
10. (-5, 1) _____

BONUS ROUND!
Write the letters in order for a surprise message!

___ ___ ___ ___   ___ ___   ___ ___ ___ ___ !
 1   2   3   4   5   6   7   8   9   10

READING TABLES AND GRAPHS

Student Enrollment	
Name of School	Number of Students
Allenville	345
Tappan	412
Old Town	550
Bellville	469

Answer these questions by looking at the table above.

1. How many students attend the Tappan school? _____
2. How many more students attend the Old Town school than the Allenville school? _____
3. Which school has the lowest enrollment? _____
4. How many students attend all four schools combined? _____
5. What is the mean enrollment of all four schools? _____

Answer these questions by looking at the graph below.

6. Which month had the most snowfall? _____
7. Which month had the least snowfall? _____
8. In which months was there more snow than rain? _____, _____
9. How much rain fell in April? _____
10. How much rain fell during the five-month period from December to April? _____
11. In which month was the snowfall and rainfall equal? _____

Key
Snow
Rain

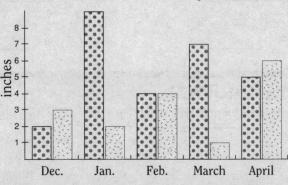

ONE-MINUTE
ENGLISH
CHALLENGES

Hooray for Homonyms!

A homonym is a word that sounds the same as another word or words but has a different meaning and is spelled differently. Read the sentence, then circle the correct homonym to fit the definition. How many can you correctly circle in one minute?

1. Is it rude to STAIR or STARE?
2. Is a teddy a BARE or BEAR?
3. Is a buzzing insect a BEE or BE?
4. Do you sail out to SEE or SEA?
5. If you've gotten bigger, have you GROWN or GROAN?
6. Is money borrowed a LONE or a LOAN?
7. Does blood go through a VANE, VEIN, or VAIN?
8. Is the horse's hair a MAINE, MANE, or MAIN?
9. Are seven days a WEAK or WEEK?
10. Will you climb to a mountain's PEEK or PEAK?
11. Do you eat a STAKE or STEAK?
12. Will a window BRAKE or BREAK?
13. Is the glass a PAIN or PANE?
14. Does the king REIN, REIGN, or RAIN?
15. Do clocks strike on the OUR or HOUR?
16. Is bread made with FLOUR or FLOWER?
17. If you change the color, do you DYE or DIE?
18. If you are near are you BUY or BY?

19. Is money owed DEW or DUE?

20. Is a female sheep a YOU or EWE?

21. Is clothing what you WARE or WEAR?

22. Do bald men lack HARE or HAIR?

23. Is to carry to HALL or HAUL?

24. Is to cry to BALL or BAWL?

25. Does a chimney have a FLUE or FLEW?

26. Is also TWO, TO, or TOO?

27. Is a man in armor a NIGHT or KNIGHT?

28. Is a letter what you RIGHT or WRITE?

29. When the game is over have you ONE or WON?

30. Is the greatest star the SUN or SON?

31. When your voice is scratchy are you HORSE or HOARSE?

32. When something's rough is it COURSE or COARSE?

33. When you listen do you HEAR or HERE?

34. Does the boat dock at the PIER or PEER?

35. Is all of something HOLE or WHOLE?

36. Is a part in a play a ROLL or ROLE?

37. Do you breathe the HEIR or AIR?

38. Do you eat a PAIR, PARE, or PEAR?

39. Is a bucket a PALE or PAIL?

40. Will the boat have a SALE or SAIL?

BONUS ROUND!

If you finished in less than a minute, try these bonus questions for extra points!

41. Popcorn has a COLONEL or KERNEL?

42. Is a youngster a MINOR or MINER?

CONTRACTION DISTRACTION!

A contraction is one word made from two words by leaving out
one or more letters and replacing them with an apostrophe (').
See how many contractions you can correctly make in one minute.

1. let us _____

2. he is _____

3. they have _____

4. were not _____

5. here is _____

6. she is _____

7. they are _____

8. what is _____

9. has not _____

10. we will _____

11. that is _____

12. do not _____

13. cannot _____

14. I would _____

15. they will _____

16. you will _____

17. I have _____

18. it is _____

19. you are _____

20. did not _____

21. she will _____

22. you have _____

23. are not _____

24. there is _____

25. I will _____

26. is not _____

27. who is _____

28. will not _____

29. was not _____

30. she would_____

31. does not _____

32. he will _____

BONUS ROUND!

If you finished in less than a minute, try these bonus questions
for extra points! Change the contraction back into two words.

33. haven't _____

34. you'll _____

35. we've _____

36. couldn't _____

37. they'd _____

38. shouldn't _____

Exciting, Incredible, Fabulous Adjective Word Search

An adjective is a word that describes something or somebody. Using the list of adjectives here, how many can you find and circle in one minute? Look for adjectives going up, down, backward, forward, and diagonally.

Adjective List:

hot	blue	slippery	tired	dirty
greasy	crisp	rough	baked	big
old	many	early	funny	bitter
noisy	fat	long	ten	bad
wet	used	dim	scared	red
soft	white	sad	top	ripe
sweet	fast			

```
S W E E T E T I H W Y
G L O N G I B X Z B S
R T I R E D E K A B I
E M E P I R E D J I O
A A I R P S I R C T N
S N T D F E U L B T Y
Y Y F O E A R L Y E N
S P O T H N T Y X R N
A L S C A R E D E S U
D R O U G H W T S A F
```

49

Rhyme Time

Are you a poet but you don't know it? Here's your chance to show it! Set the timer for one minute. Then see how many words rhyming with the word *GREAT* you can write down before your time is up.

GREAT

1. _____ 2. _____ 3. _____ 4. _____

5. _____ 6. _____ 7. _____ 8. _____

9. _____ 10. _____ 11. _____ 12. _____

13. _____ 14. _____ 15. _____ 16. _____

17. _____ 18. _____ 19. _____ 20. _____

21. _____ 22. _____ 23. _____ 24. _____

25. _____ 26. _____ 27. _____ 28. _____

29. _____ 30. _____

BONUS ROUND!

If you thought of 30 words in less than a minute, your bonus round is this: TAKE A WELL-DESERVED REST!

Or, quickly, in the time you have left write down ten words that rhyme with the word REST.

1. _____ 2. _____ 3. _____ 4. _____

5. _____ 6. _____ 7. _____ 8. _____

9. _____ 10. _____

Shhhh! Silent Letter Zone!

There are 26 letters in the alphabet. For as many letters of the alphabet as possible, try to find a word in which that letter is silent. See how many you can write down in one minute. (Example: in Zone, the *e* is silent.)

A _____   B _____   C _____

D _____   E _____   F _____

G _____   H _____   I _____

J _____   K _____   L _____

M _____   N _____   O _____

P _____   Q _____   R _____

S _____   T _____   U _____

V _____   W _____   X _____

Y _____   Z _____

PALINDROME CROSSWORD

A palindrome is a word, phrase, verse, or sentence that reads the same way backward as it does forward. The answers in this crossword puzzle are all one-word palindromes (except for one tricky answer). Use the clues to help you. Give yourself a minute and see how much of the puzzle you can complete. (If time runs out, finish it just for fun.)

Across
1. Slang for mother.
3. A formal way to address a woman.
5. A firecracker that won't pop.
6. Slang for statistics.
8. Songs sung alone.
10. You see with it.

Down
2. To be silent.
4. Slang for father.
5. A bird that is extinct.
7. Slang for a girl sibling.
9. Even, flat.
11. The night before Christmas.

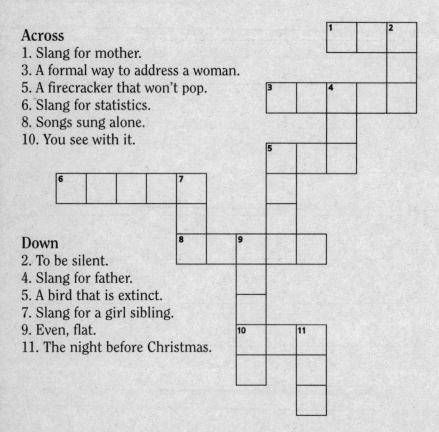

EI, IE, OH NO!

You know the old *i* before *e* rule, right? "Put *i* before *e* except after *c*, or when sounded like *a* as in *neighbor* and *weigh*." Sound easy? Fill in the blanks with either *ie* or *ei* to complete the words correctly. How many can you do in one minute? (*Hint*: It may be helpful to say the words out loud. If there is a word you don't know, go on to the next one. Remember, every second counts!)

1. n____ther
2. gr____ve
3. v____w
4. br____f
5. ch____f
6. h____ght
7. fr____nd
8. bel____ve
9. conc____t
10. b____ge
11. rel____f
12. c____ling
13. misch____f
14. p____ce
15. s____ze
16. forf____t
17. prot____n

18. anc____nt
19. sl____ght
20. dec____ve
21. rec____pt
22. sh____ld
23. caff____ne
24. pr____st
25. th____f
26. r____gn
27. f____ld
28. hyg____ne
29. s____ge
30. sover____gn
31. glac____r
32. sc____nce
33. spec____s
34. h____r

35. r____ndeer
36. w____ght
37. n____ghbor
38. cash____r
39. consc____nce
40. gr____f
41. bes____ge
42. s____ve
43. w____rd
44. bel____f
45. p____rce
46. shr____k
47. front____r
48. effic____nt
49. counterf____t
50. ach____ve

Word Rebus Riddles

These word pictures are called rebuses. Each rebus is a riddle. Your job is to see how many rebus riddles you can solve in a minute. Study each word rebus and try to figure out what the word picture stands for.

An example is: $\dfrac{\text{MAN}}{\text{BOARD}}$ = MAN OVERBOARD

1.
```
    R
    O
R O A D S
    D
    S
```

2.
```
GROUND
 FEET
 FEET
 FEET
 FEET
 FEET
 FEET
```

3.
```
T
O
U
C
H
```

---

4. <u>SIGN</u>............

5.

6.
```
ONE    ANOTHER
ONE    ANOTHER
ONE    ANOTHER
ONE    ANOTHER
ONE    ANOTHER
ONE    ANOTHER
```

---

7. ONAHOLEE

8.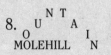

9.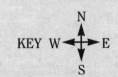

54

State Abbreviations

Through wind, rain, sleet, or snow, the mail must go through! To help the mail go through faster, the postal service requires two-letter abbreviations for the states. How many of the 50 states can you correctly abbreviate in one minute?

____Alabama	____Louisiana	____Ohio
____Alaska	____Maine	____Oklahoma
____Arizona	____Maryland	____Oregon
____Arkansas	____Massachusetts	____Pennsylvania
____California	____Michigan	____Rhode Island
____Colorado	____Minnesota	____South Carolina
____Connecticut	____Mississippi	____South Dakota
____Delaware	____Missouri	____Tennessee
____Florida	____Montana	____Texas
____Georgia	____Nebraska	____Utah
____Hawaii	____Nevada	____Vermont
____Idaho	____New Hampshire	____Virginia
____Illinois	____New Jersey	____Washington
____Indiana	____New Mexico	____West Virginia
____Iowa	____New York	____Wisconsin
____Kansas	____North Carolina	____Wyoming
____Kentucky	____North Dakota	

BONUS ROUND!

If you finished in less than a minute, try abbreviating these territories and districts.

____Canal Zone   ____District of Columbia   ____Guam
____Puerto Rico   ____Virgin Islands

A Capital Offense!

Read the story once before you set the timer. Then, set the timer for one minute and circle each letter you find that needs capitalizing. When one minute is up, count the circles you've made. Remember to look for first words in a sentence, names of people and places, the pronoun I, and words of family relationships when used as a person's name.

the thing in the lake

on saturday, july 14, mom, dad, and i drove to sebago lake. i was hoping the morris family and their big bully of a son, butch, wouldn't be there waiting for us. well, butch was there all right, but so was something else. everybody was talking about the monster in the lake.

"sheriff johnson and his deputy stayed up all night watching for it," said butch's aunt harriet. "they're calling the thing nessie, after the loch ness monster. if you ask me, i think it's just a big old carp."

"no child of mine is going to be bait for a lake monster," mom told dad. "i think we should get in the car and go back home to our house on pine street in our safe little town of pine bluffs, massachusetts. the only monsters there are the dust balls under the bed!"

just as i was about to complain, i turned for one last look at sebago lake. guess what i saw waving at me from out in the middle of the lake? butch morris, who else. it was all his idea of one big joke. the laugh was on him, though, because right behind him something else was waving, too. it was nessie, the thing in the lake! when butch saw the monster behind him, he swam ashore as fast as he could.

butch and his family left and never came back to the lake. as for mom, dad, and me, we stayed and had the best summer ever. butch's aunt was right. the "monster" was just a big fish. it's in an aquarium in boston now. thanks to the monster, the really scary thing in the lake is gone! bye, butch. i don't miss you at all!

Two Words = One

Compound words are two words combined to make one. Draw a line from the sets of five words in Column A to the five words in Column B to make as many sets of compound words as you can in one minute.

Column A	Column B
1. arm	worm
down	person
bare	chair
earth	pour
chair	back
2. tear	tag
birth	bird
name	wide
black	drop
world	place
3. score	paper
knap	wreck
knock	card
news	out
ship	sack
4. text	case
broom	light
flag	stick
suit	book
moon	pole
5. team	born
street	mate
new	car
chalk	work
play	board

Scrambled Words

Unscramble the three letters on the left and write a new word in the space on the right. How many new words can you make in a minute? yTr ti! (That's "Try it!")

hwo	tra	yna
atc	oer	dha
xob	rac	ent
dna	tib	ubn
pil	dlo	tho
rae	tha	oto
upt	atp	nwo
usb	gub	fde
mmo	ubt	gdi
wot	pag	eeb
unt	rof	anp
kao	arf	yee
eon	ufn	rao
pho	nug	ozo
wes	eus	pma
nam	hes	dba

BONUS ROUND!

If you finished them all in less than a minute, try these four-letter words for extra fun.

ndah	adeh
raih	lpeh

WORD IN A WORD

Each capitalized word has another word hidden in it. The clues will help you find the hidden words. Underline them. How many can you find in one minute?

Find a winged thing in BEAT,
And an auto in CARE.
Something warm is in WHEAT,
A long distance in FAIR.
There's a bug tucked in PANT,
And a boy's name in BEAN.
Find a plot in a PLANT,
And a number in TEEN.
There's a nap in CREST,
And a tool in SHOE.
A direction's in WREST.
More than one is in FLEW.
Find a fruit in APPEAR,
And a listener in HEAR.
There's a buddy in PAIL,
And a good buy in SCALE.
Something legal's in CLAW,
Something uncooked in DRAW.
There's a question in CHOW,
Something not high in PLOW.
Two times five is in TREND,
And the last line's in SEND.

LET'S COMPARE PAIRS

An analogy is a comparison between two pairs of items. The first pair of items is related in the same way as the second pair. For example:

HARD is to ROCK as SOFT is to COTTON.

Use the words in the word bank to finish each analogy. Set the timer for one minute and complete as many as you can.

Word Bank

floor	hat	taste	water	vegetable
empty	ship	down	enclosing	painting
sled	eleventh	swimming	thermometer	glove

1. BLOUSE is to SHIRT as BONNET is to _____.

2. WRITER is to BOOK as ARTIST is to _____.

3. BIRD is to FLYING as FISH is to _____.

4. WALLPAPER is to WALL as RUG is to _____.

5. TRUTH is to LIE as FULL is to _____.

6. APPLE is to FRUIT as CORN is to _____.

7. NOSE is to SMELL as TONGUE is to _____.

8. KNIFE is to CUTTING as FENCE is to _____.

9. CAR is to LAND as BOAT is to _____.

10. ASTRONAUT is to SPACESHIP as SAILOR is to_____.

11. HEAD is to HELMET as HAND is to _____.

12. NONSENSE is to SENSE as UP is to _____.

13. SECOND is to THIRD as TENTH is to _____.

14. HORSE is to CARRIAGE as DOG is to _____.

15. TIME is to CLOCK as TEMPERATURE is to _____.

Homonym Crossword

All of the answers in this crossword puzzle are homonyms, words that sound the same but are spelled differently from the clues below and have different meanings. Set your timer for one minute and try to beat the clock!

Across
3. GROWN
4. WEIGHT
6. BEE
7. MEET
9. ORE and OR
10. DO or DEW

Down
1. FOUR and FORE
2. NOT
4. WE
5. SEA
6. BOARD
8. TWO and TOO

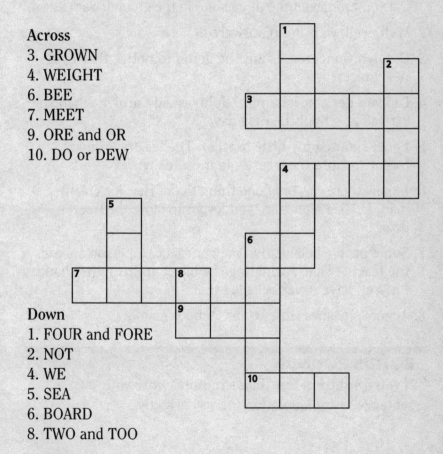

NOTABLE QUOTES

Of course you know quotation marks are used to enclose a speaker's exact words. Using that rule, take one minute to place quotation marks correctly in the following sentences.

1. Did you hear about the three holes in the ground? Sam asked.

2. Well, well, well, John answered.

3. Carolyn wondered, Is anyone going to notice that I got new braces?

4. Did you get a new haircut? John asked Carolyn when she arrived at school the next day.

5. Look! shouted my little brother. The ice cream man forgot to close the freezer door on his truck!

6. I knew there was only one thing to do. Hey, ice cream man, I called after him, you forgot to close the freezer door!

7. Some people believe that pepper makes a person sneeze, the teacher said, sprinkling the black grains in her hand. I myself have never believed that.

8. Achoo! she sneezed. Achoo! Achoo! Achoo!

BONUS ROUND!

If you finished in less than a minute, write your own sentence, using quotation marks correctly.

ALPHABET SOUP

What's your initial response to this first initials test? Each set of initials stands for the same thing the number equals. The first one has been done for you. How many of the rest can you guess in a minute?

1. 26 = L of the A   <u>Letters of the Alphabet</u>

2. 4 and 20 = B B in a P   <u>   </u>

3. 9 = P in the S S   <u>   </u>

4. 24 = H in a D   <u>   </u>

5. 12 = M in the Y   <u>   </u>

6. 7 = D in a W   <u>   </u>

7. 4 = Q in a G   <u>   </u>

8. 13 = S on the U.S. F   <u>   </u>

9. 52 (53) = C in a D (with the J) <u>   </u>

10. 90 = D in a R A   <u>   </u>

11. 11 = P on a F T   <u>   </u>

12. 3 = B M "S H T R"   <u>   </u>

SIMILES

A simile is a figure of speech that compares one thing to another using the word "like" or "as." The similes here have been split up. Draw a line from Column A to Column B to match the first part of a simile to the word that correctly finishes it. How many can you complete in one minute?

Column A	Column B
Blind as a	pancake.
Dead as a	bug in a rug.
Cold as	fruitcake.
Flat as a	tack.
Quiet as a	peacock.
Snug as a	pig.
Old as the	doornail.
Sly as a	ice.
Neat as a	bee.
Light as a	molasses.
Fit as a	fox.
Busy as a	mouse.
Slow as	pin.
Fat as a	bat.
Proud as a	hills.
Nutty as a	feather.
Sharp as a	fiddle.

What's Unusual About This Paragraph?

In the paragraph below there is something quite unusual. Set the timer for one minute. Read the paragraph over and over and see if you can solve this mystery before your time is up.

A Most Unusual Paragraph

What is so unusual about this paragraph? You won't find too many paragraphs similar to it. Look at it and study it. You may not find out what is unusual right away. Study it again. At first you may fail in your task. But if you stay with it you will find a solution. Think. What is odd about it? Look and look again. Do you want a hint? Sorry. No hints for you today or tomorrow. You must do this without asking for hints. It's a most unusual paragraph, would you not say so? But why? That's what you must find out now. Good luck!

Write your answer here:

_____

To -GE or Not to -DGE?
That Is the Question!

At the end of a word, the "j" sound can be spelled -*ge* or -*dge*.
-*Dge* is used at the end of a word or syllable directly after a single
short vowel. -*Ge* is used after a consonant, after a long vowel
sound, and after two vowels. Those are the rules to follow as you
see how many of the words here are spelled correctly. Write T for
True if a word is spelled right, and F for False if it's spelled wrong.
Ready? Set the timer for one minute, then begin!

1.____brige	12.____bage	23.____range
2.____age	13.____huge	24.____smudge
3.____juge	14.____radge	25.____stage
4.____porrige	15.____arrange	26.____urdge
5.____hinge	16.____verdge	27.____dredge
6.____knowlege	17.____merdge	28.____fuge
7.____strange	18.____truge	29.____doge
8.____goudge	19.____sponge	30.____cartrige
9.____fordge	20.____page	31.____change
10.____rige	21.____couradge	32.____lardge
11.____cadge	22.____plege	33.____partrige

BONUS ROUND!

If you finished this in less than a minute, try these for
extra fun: 34. ____Anchoradge 35. ____Dodgers

SLING THE SLANG

Slang words or expressions are colorful and exaggerated ways of saying ordinary things. For example, if someone is acting strangely, there are many slang expressions to describe that behavior—"He's gone bananas!" or "She's lost her marbles!" or "They must be nuts!" How well can you sling the slang around? Take one minute to test yourself. See how many slang words or expressions you can correctly match to their definitions. Write the letter of the slang in the numbered space next to its definition.

Slang

A. Get the lead out.

B. Not playing with a full deck.

C. Chill out.

D. Straight from the horse's mouth.

E. Out in left field.

F. Pull the wool over one's eyes.

G. Up a creek without a paddle.

H. Two shakes of a lamb's tail.

I. Tickle the ivories.

J. There you go.

K. Spill the beans.

L. John Hancock.

M. Hood.

N. Earbender.

O. Circular file.

P. Throw in the towel.

Q. Zilch.

Definition

_____1. To reveal the secret.

_____2. To hurry.

_____3. One who talks too much.

_____4. Entirely mistaken.

_____5. Nothing.

_____6. Wastebasket.

_____7. Absent-minded.

_____8. One's signature.

_____9. Neighborhood.

_____10. To admit defeat.

_____11. Troublesome situation.

_____12. In a very short time.

_____13. Play the piano.

_____14. Relax.

_____15. To deceive.

_____16. Now you've got it.

_____17. From the original source.

BONUS ROUND!

If you finished in less than a minute, write three slang words or expressions which mean "great!" or "very good!"

1._____ 2._____ 3._____

Drop-a-Letter, Find-a-Word

Use the first clue to help you figure out the first word in the pair. Then let the second clue help you decide which letter to drop to make a new word. Set the timer for one minute (what else!) and make as many new words as possible before the time is up.

1. A girl getting married is called a _____.
   Drop a letter and go for a _____.

2. Soap and water will get you _____.
   Drop a letter; you're not fat, you're _____!

3. If you want to sweep, use a _____.
   Drop a letter and go to your _____.

4. When you're thirsty get yourself a _____.
   Drop a letter for an ice-skating _____.

5. Before you buy, check the tag for the _____.
   Drop a letter for a white food called _____.

6. To stop the car, step on the _____.
   Drop a letter for a garden _____.

7. When you fly you ride in a big air _____.
   Drop a letter for a walk down the _____.

8. A man wearing armor is called a _____.
   Drop a letter and say "good-_____."

9. Beef and pork are two kinds of _____.
   Drop a letter, now it's time to _____!

10. Boil the water and up rises the _____.
    Drop a letter and cheer for your _____!

11. Look! Up in the sky there's a fluffy white, _____!
    Drop a letter for a noise that is _____.

12. Exercise can make muscles feel _____.
    Drop a letter for some iron _____.

13. A thing that says, "Boo!" is called a _____.
    Drop a letter for a talk show _____.

14. If it's all your fault, then take all the _____.
    Drop a letter for a hurt leg that's _____.

15. If you're hungry, pile food on your _____.
    Drop a letter to be tardy or _____.

16. A party for sleeping is sometimes called "_____."
    Drop a letter and another name for wood is _____.

17. A lobster's hand is called a _____.
    Drop a letter and obey the _____!

18. Hurry now, you're almost _____.
    Drop a letter, this is the last _____!

Just Say NO!

There's a NO in every word in this challenge. Read the definitions and fill in the blanks to complete the NO words. Can you do them all in one minute? Say YES to NO!

1. Opposite of something.   N O __ __ __ __ __

2. Handle on a door.   __ N O __

3. A banana-shaped boat you paddle.   __ __ N O __

4. A prehistoric animal.   __ __ N O __ __ __ __

5. It's on your face and smells.   N O __ __

6. Opposite of majority.   __ __ N O __ __ __ __

7. A judge is called "Your_____."   __ __ N O __

8. A short letter.   N O __ __

9. White flakes in winter.   __ N O __

10. The opposite of major.   __ __ N O __

11. The right amount.   __ N O __ __ __

12. To bother.   __ __ N O __

13. A musical instrument with 88 keys.   __ __ __ N O

14. Opposite of sense.   N O __ __ __ __ __ __

15. Can't is the contraction.   __ __ __ N O __

MORE REBUS RIDDLES

Each rebus is a riddle. How many riddles can you guess in one minute?

1.

2.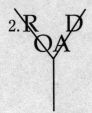

3.
L

O

W

_____

_____

_____

4.

   ado   ado
ado nothing
         ado
  ado   ado

5.

6.   POLE

N
W + E
S

_____

_____

_____

7.   CYCLE
     CYCLE
     CYCLE

8. N   T
    W   O
    O   W
    T   N

9.
N
W + E
S
GONE

_____

_____

_____

BONUS ROUND!

If you finished in less than a minute, make up a rebus of your own for extra fun.

THE NAME OF THE GAME IS NOUN HUNT

A noun is the name of a person, place, or thing. Find and underline the nouns in the sentences below. How many can you find in one minute?

1. Corey plays tennis every day.

2. Will he win this tennis match?

3. The score is 15–40, match point.

4. Both players wipe the sweat off their faces with their sleeves.

5. The ground feels hard under Corey's feet.

6. The ball bounces halfway between the baseline and the service line.

7. He swings his racket at the ball and makes contact.

8. "Wow!" Corey thinks to himself. "I won the match!"

BONUS ROUND!

If you finished in less than a minute, find and underline the nouns in this bonus sentence:

Practice is the most important part of every player's game.

Just the Opposite!

All the answers in this challenge are opposites, or antonyms. Use the clues to help you correctly unscramble the letters and spell each opposite word. Write the new words in the spaces provided. How many can you do before one minute is up?

1. fast   wlos   _____
2. cold   tho   _____
3. open   secol   _____
4. dirty   lanec   _____
5. soft   drah   _____
6. empty   lufl   _____
7. small   gbi   _____
8. happy   das   _____
9. nervous   mcal   _____
10. tall   hrtos   _____
11. fat   htni   _____
12. borrow   nedl   _____
13. take   egiv   _____
14. sour   estwe   _____
15. weak   grtsno   _____
16. awake   peelsa   _____
17. floor   lcneigi   _____
18. love   ehta   _____
19. go   sopt   _____
20. beginning   dne   _____
21. death   file   _____
22. good   vile   _____
23. man   nwmoa   _____
24. dark   gtlhi   _____
25. true   slfea   _____

Ken Ewe Reed?

These sentences are written completely in homonyms. As they are written, they make no sense. How many can you correctly translate into homonyms that will make sense? Set your timer for one minute and begin.

1. Ken ewe reed?

_____

2. Eye sea too oar for flours.

_____

3. Witch which bytes end witch won Ken knot?

_____

4. Dew groan bares grown?

_____

5. Know won nose weather ore knot ate ours past.

_____

6. Hoarse heards flu buy!

_____

7. Won knight eye herd sum belles wring.

_____

-OUGHT OR *-AUGHT*? YOU OUGHT TO KNOW!

This story ought to be completed in one minute or less. As you read it, fill in the blanks with either *aught* or *ought*. Then read the story again.

C_____ in the Rain

"Oh no!" said Mrs. Minshall's youngest d_____er. "It's starting to rain! We should have br_____ an umbrella."

"Don't worry, dear," her mother said th_____fully. "I never get c_____ without one. If you hold this bag of things I just b_____, I'm sure I'll find the umbrella in my other bag."

"Hurry up, Mom," snapped the d_____er h_____ily. "I t_____ you to be patient," replied Mrs. Minshall. "That tone of voice is not nice. Don't you be a n_____y girl."

"I'm sorry, Mom," replied the girl. The two of them never f_____ about something as silly as getting c_____ in the rain.

In a minute Mrs. Minshall found the thing she s_____. "Here it is!" She smiled happily, holding up the umbrella. "I th_____ I'd find it. And if I didn't I would have b_____ another one!"

BONUS ROUND!

If you finished in less than a minute, try this extra sentence for extra fun:

Vegetarians are t_____ not to sl_____er the animals they've c_____.

More Alphabet Soup

Each set of initials stands for the same thing the number equals. See how many you can guess before one minute is up.

1. 1,001 = A N _____

2. 18 = H on a G C _____

3. 200 = D for P G in M _____

4. 5 = D in a Z C _____

5. 10 = L I B _____

6. 29 = D in F in a L Y _____

7. 57 = H V _____

8. 2 = W on a B _____

9. 9 = I in a B G _____

10. 32 = D F at which W F _____

11. 50 = S on the U.S. F _____

12. 2 = S to E S _____

WORD PYRAMIDS

Use the clues to help you fill in the blanks. Start at the top of
each word pyramid. Add one letter in each step down. How many
word pyramids can you build in a minute?

G

___ ___
Ready, set, ____!

___ ___ ___
Already received.

___ ___ ___ ___
Farm or mountain animal.

___ ___ ___ ___ ___
Think about with mean pleasure.

O

___ ___
Either, ___

___ ___ ___
Rowing tool.

___ ___ ___ ___
Wild pig.

___ ___ ___ ___ ___
Wooden plank.

T

___ ___
Homonym for two or too.

___ ___ ___
2,000 pounds = 1 ____

___ ___ ___ ___
Musical sound or make a muscle.

___ ___ ___ ___ ___
A rock.

H

___ ___
A laugh.

___ ___ ___
Sandwich meat.

___ ___ ___ ___
Hurt.

___ ___ ___ ___ ___
Small lucky symbol.

H

___ ___
Him.

___ ___ ___
She.

___ ___ ___ ___
Listen and catch sound.

___ ___ ___ ___ ___
Valentine shape.

A

___ ___
One ___ a time.

___ ___ ___
Hunger solution.

___ ___ ___ ___
Sit on it.

___ ___ ___ ___ ___
Perspire.

Spell Check

Find the word in each group that is spelled correctly. Circle the letter in front of the correctly spelled word in each row. Set your timer for one minute and begin.

1. a. atic   b. attick   c. attic   d. adik
2. a. canoo   b. canue   c. cano   d. canoe
3. a. answer   b. ansur   c. anser   d. ansure
4. a. lauf   b. laff   c. laugh   d. laffe
5. a. prety   b. pritty   c. priddy   d. pretty
6. a. sootcase   b. suitcase   c. suitcays   d. sutcase
7. a. scard   b. scaired   c. scared   d. skared
8. a. ekwel   b. equal   c. eekwall   d. eakqual
9. a. senior   b. senure   c. seenior   d. seanure
10. a. acke   b. ake   c. ache   d. eake
11. a. recipee   b. resipe   c. ressipee   d. recipe
12. a. salid   b. saled   c. salad   d. salade
13. a. yaght   b. yacht   c. yaught   d. yaht
14. a. fasten   b. fassen   c. fastin   d. fassin
15. a. antike   b. anteque   c. antique   d. anteek
16. a. plummer   b. plomber   c. plumger   d. plumber
17. a. gess   b. gues   c. guess   d. gesse
18. a. twelth   b. twelfth   c. twellfth   d. twelphth
19. a. pome   b. poam   c. powem   d. poem
20. a. scissers   b. scissors   c. scizzors   d. siccors

78

Find the Fragments

Every sentence should tell a complete thought. A fragment does not tell a complete thought. Read the sentences below. Set the timer for one minute. How many sentences and fragments can you correctly identify in the time allowed? Write S for sentence and F for fragment in the space before each group of words.

_____1. Kip plays shortstop on his school's baseball team.

_____2. Sewing with a needle and thread.

_____3. Lauren on the roller coaster.

_____4. My cousin and I.

_____5. Go to your room!

_____6. Empty pockets, empty wallets.

_____7. All the way home.

_____8. The fun is just beginning.

_____9. Call me in the morning.

_____10. Stop!

_____11. Never say never.

_____12. The sled in the snow.

_____13. Some say thirteen is an unlucky number.

_____14. It isn't.

_____15. Who wants more?

_____16. Music on the radio.

_____17. Change the channel.

_____18. Why do you cry?

_____19. If the shoe fits, wear it.

_____20. A sentence has a subject and a predicate.

COMMAS, THE PAUSES THAT REFRESH

Commas make a reader pause when reading. Use a comma
to separate items in dates and items in addresses. Use a
comma after *yes, no, ah, oh,* and *well* when these words
begin a sentence. Use these rules to help you correctly place
commas where they belong in the sentences below. Set the
timer for one minute and begin.

1. Yes I did say I'd meet him on July 25 1999.
2. I sent a letter to Mr. Coleman's house at 25 Pine Street
   Evansville Virginia.
3. Oh I wouldn't be too sure about that!
4. Well we missed the boat.
5. No we don't plan to move from Boston Massachusetts to New
   York New York.
6. Ah you mean you remember the parade on Monday July 4 1985?
7. So do you think your team will win this year?
8. Philadelphia Pennsylvania has many sights to see.
9. Yes we are planning a reunion on December 7 2002.
10. Oh who can possibly remember all the names of all the states?

BONUS ROUND!

If you finished in less than a minute, add the commas to these
sentences for extra fun.

My grandmother was born February 16 1938 in Portland
Maine. Oh how she loves that town!
"Yes I think this is the best place in the world!" she says.

ACTION VERBS FOR ACTIVE PEOPLE

Words that add action to a sentence are called action verbs. These verbs tell about action you can see (for example: run, jump, laugh) and about action you cannot see (for example: like, think, believe). Set the timer for one minute. Then underline the action verbs in the sentences below.

1. Martin Luther King Jr. dreamed of freedom for all people.

2. Thomas Jefferson wrote the Declaration of Independence.

3. Albert Einstein thought too much in class.

4. Mark Twain worked on a riverboat on the Mississippi River.

5. Even though she was blind, Helen Keller was able to read, write, and finish college.

6. Grandma Moses painted until her hands were too weak to hold a brush.

7. Wolfgang Mozart composed music when he was five years old.

8. Marco Polo traveled from Venice to China.

9. Eleanor Roosevelt carried the message of world peace wherever she spoke.

10. Chief Joseph wished his people did not have to fight for their land.

11. Harry Houdini made his audiences believe in magic.

12. Benjamin Franklin taught himself algebra, geometry, science, logic, writing, grammar, and five foreign languages.

Magic Squares

The answers in these crosswords are the same across and down. Read the clues and fill in as many Magic Squares as you can in one minute.

1. Spoiled child.
2. Wealthy.
3. A pain.
4. Opposite of now.

1. A present.
2. A thought.
3. To touch.
4. Opposite of short.

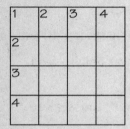

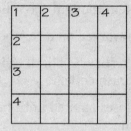

1. Winter white stuff.
2. Three times three.
3. One less than twice.
4. Seven days equal one.

1. _____, crackle, pop!
2. What you call yourself.
3. Prayer ending.
4. Ink-filled writing instruments

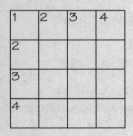

State Stumper

The names of 15 states are hidden in the sentences below. Underline them as you find them. Your one-minute time limit begins right . . . NOW!

1. Is that terrible bore gone yet?

2. "Mama, I need a new bicycle," said the little boy.

3. We saw the color ad on the front page of the newspaper.

4. "Oh, I only like mustard on hot dogs," my uncle said.

5. Put a ham in the shopping cart.

6. I see the lovely miss is sipping soda through a straw.

7. Will Al ask a doctor about that pain in his neck?

8. I sure miss our incredible teacher, don't you?

9. Where did Mary land her plane after the transatlantic flight?

10. The new beach has a Wade Law, a Read Law, and a Sand Castle Law.

11. I want a large or giant box of chocolates to share with my friends.

12. Before I connect, I cut the wires and tape the ends.

13. Ken, tuck your shirt in please!

14. If Lori dares to speak out in class, she'll be sent to the office again.

15. "I feel ill," I noisily complained to the flight attendant.

ORDER IN THE ALPHABET!

Putting words in alphabetical order can be tricky. Set the timer for one minute, then see how many groups of words below you can put in alphabetical order before your time is up. Number the words in the order you choose.

1	2	3	4
flies	sponge	talent	bones
dirt	squash	tall	broken
files	summer	talk	about
deal	spoken	telephone	above
field	snow	under	best
drip	swing	silly	bacon

5	6	7	8
chapter	open	match	defeat
calendar	pencil	name	deduct
chord	peninsula	nurse	defense
chance	opera	mound	detail
dreary	operation	movie	delete
dresser	odor	mark	delight

BONUS ROUND!

If you finished in less than a minute, try these for extra fun. If you alphabetize them correctly you'll read a surprise message!

learn
all
well
kids
very

ANSWERS

page 6

1. 678; 2. 974; 3. 999; 4. 998; 5. 797; 6. 749; 7. 998; 8. 978; 9. 869; 10. 969.
Bonus Round: 956; 898; 1,189; 1,265.

page 7

1. 86,988; 2. 679,708; 3. 68,488; 4. 665,978; 5. 39,948; 6. 978,878; 7. 86,767; 8. 888,356; 9. 885,583; 10. 46,626.
Bonus Round: 1,037,785; 176,799; 176,475; 97,999.

page 8

1. 8,801; 2. 4,591; 3. 8,913; 4. 7,907; 5. 71,892; 6. 92,910; 7. 83,179; 8. 89,681.
Bonus Round: 75,052; 11,531; 5,926; 14,027.

page 9

1. 92; 2. 112; 3. 115; 4. 107; 5. 1,070; 6. 1,147; 7. 13,431; 8. 12,223.
Bonus Round:

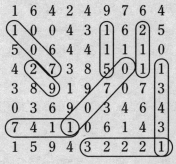

page 10

1. 4,895; 2. 6,231; 3. 28,498

page 11

1. 2,150; 2. 1,234; 3. 435; 4. 2,120; 5. 4,551; 6. 1,112; 7. 1,412; 8. 1,111; 9. 1,202; 10. 1,201; 11. 5,021; 12. 4,445; 13. 3,200; 14. 322.

page 12

1. 25; 2. 152; 3. 398; 4. 1,802; 5. 74; 6. 150; 7. 2,578.
Bonus Round: 2,930; 3,644; 313; 1,313.

page 13
1. 2,622; 2. 553; 3. 739; 4. 1,433.
Bonus Round: 5,308.

page 14
1. 20; 2. 200; 3. 490; 4. 150; 5. 600; 6. 3,600; 7. 4,200; 8. 4,800; 9. 84;
10. 69; 11. 168; 12. 213; 13. 1,266; 14. 1,300.

page 15
1. 1,802; 2. 1,600; 3. 1,012; 4. 1,827; 5. 2,368; 6. 3,330; 7. 2,349;
8. 1,105; 9. 2,538; 10. 2,178.

page 16
1. 7 r.1; 2. 24 r.1; 3. 9 r.3; 4. 16 r.2; 5. 217 r.2; 6. 129 r.5; 7. 130 r.3;
8. 102 r.1; 9. 84 r.1; 10. 96 r.5.

page 17
1. <; 2. >; 3. =; 4. >; 5. >; 6. >; 7. =; 8. >; 9. <; 10. >; 11. <; 12. =;
13. >; 14. >; 15. <; 16. <.

page 18
1. 178; 2. 445; 3. $709; 4. 600; 5. 226; 6. 557.

page 19
1. $1\frac{1}{5}$; 2. $1\frac{2}{5}$; 3. 2; 4. $2\frac{1}{4}$; 5. 2; 6. $1\frac{3}{4}$; 7. 2; 8. $2\frac{2}{3}$; 9. $2\frac{1}{2}$; 10. $2\frac{1}{3}$; 11. $1\frac{5}{7}$; 12. $2\frac{3}{4}$;
13. $2\frac{1}{7}$; 14. $2\frac{3}{5}$; 15. $2\frac{2}{7}$; 16. $4\frac{2}{3}$.

page 20
1. V; 2. X; 3. C; 4. L; 5. LX; 6. LXX; 7. LXXX; 8. CLI; 9. CCXCIII;
10. CCCXCIX.

page 21
1. 300; 2. 400; 3. 500; 4. 1,000; 5. 2,000; 6. 1,016; 7. 1,322; 8. 527;
9. 1,122; 10. 1,323.

page 22
1. millions; 2. tens; 3. hundreds; 4. hundred thousands;
5. ten thousands; 6. thousands; 7. ones; 8. thousands;
9. tens; 10. millions; 11. hundred thousands; 12. ten thousands;
13. tens; 14. thousands; 15. ones.

page 23

1. $\frac{11}{4}$; 2. $\frac{9}{2}$; 3. $\frac{11}{3}$; 4. $\frac{47}{8}$; 5. $\frac{7}{4}$; 6. $\frac{13}{5}$; 7. $\frac{4}{3}$; 8. $\frac{41}{6}$; 9. $\frac{44}{5}$; 10. $\frac{91}{12}$

Bonus Round: $\frac{79}{8}$; $\frac{25}{2}$; $\frac{20}{3}$; $\frac{44}{9}$; $\frac{143}{12}$.

page 24

1. 2,601 r.2; 2. 512 r.1; 3. 1,006 r.4; 4. 895 r.2; 5. 743 r.1.

page 25

1. Range = 35
   Mean = 65
2. Range = 19
   Mean = 31

Bonus Round: Range = 19; Mean = 88

page 26

1. $6\frac{1}{2}$; 2. $5\frac{17}{20}$; 3. $8\frac{41}{72}$; 4. $8\frac{8}{6} = 9\frac{1}{3}$; 5. $11\frac{11}{28}$; 6. $12\frac{22}{15} = 13\frac{7}{15}$.

page 27

1. $6\frac{1}{3}$; 2. $4\frac{4}{15}$; 3. $4\frac{7}{20}$; 4. $5\frac{3}{10}$; 5. $3\frac{13}{24}$; 6. $5\frac{1}{20}$; 7. $5\frac{1}{10}$; 8. $6\frac{17}{28}$.

page 28

1. $3\frac{2}{3}$; 2. 2; 3. 6; 4. $1\frac{4}{5}$; 5. $2\frac{2}{5}$.

Bonus Round: 6; $2\frac{2}{3}$; $1\frac{1}{2}$.

page 29

1. $5; 2. $145; 3. $50; 4. Courtney; 5. 9 seconds.

page 30

1. $4 \times 4 \times 4 = 64$; 2. 7; 3. $3 \times 3 \times 3 \times 3 = 81$; 4. $5 \times 5 \times 5 \times 5 \times 5 = 3,125$;
5. 0; 6. $9 \times 9 = 81$; 7. $10 \times 10 \times 10 = 1,000$; 8. $2 \times 2 \times 2 \times 2 \times 2 = 32$;
9. $6 \times 6 \times 6 \times 6 = 1,296$; 10. $8 \times 8 = 64$.

page 31

1. 5^5; 2. 4^3; 3. 9^7; 4. 7^5; 5. 6^3; 6. 2^2; 7. 4^1; 8. 3^5; 9. 8^2; 10. 7^4; 11. 11^6;
12. 19^2; 13. 23^1; 14. 5^7; 15. 2^5.

page 32

1. 2,676; 2. 3,465; 3. 4,944; 4. 4,000; 5. $124.20.

page 33

1. 11 cm; 2. 12 cm; 3. 10 in.; 4. 10 in.; 5. 178 ft.; 6. 28 ft.

page 34
1. 293 r.3; 2. 207 r.12; 3. 252 r.1; 4. 202 r.26

page 35
1. A (-3, -1); 2. B (+4, +5); 3. C (+4, -2); 4. D (+3, +2); 5. E (+1, -4);
6. F (+2, +4)
Bonus Round: 7. T; 8. H; 9. I; 10; S; 11. I; 12. S; 13. F; 14. U; 15. N.
THIS IS FUN!

page 36
1. 5:4; 2. 4:2; 3. 2:5; 4. 4:5; 5. 2:4; 6. 5:2; 7. 8:4; 8. 6:8; 9. 4:6; 10. 8:6;
11. 7:8; 12. 6:7; 13. 8:6; 14. 7:6.

page 37
1. $\frac{1}{4} = \frac{5}{20}$; 2. $\frac{2}{3} = \frac{4}{6}$; 3. $\frac{3}{4} = \frac{6}{8}$; 4. $\frac{2}{5} = \frac{4}{10}$; 5. $\frac{4}{6} = \frac{2}{3}$; 6. $\frac{3}{6} = \frac{6}{12}$; 7. $\frac{4}{20} = \frac{1}{5}$; 8. \$24; 9. \$3;
10. 40.

page 38
1. $\frac{15}{100}$ or $\frac{3}{20}$ / .15 / 15%; 2. $\frac{25}{100}$ or $\frac{1}{4}$ / .25 / 25%; 3. $\frac{35}{100}$ or $\frac{7}{20}$ / .35 / 35%

page 39
1. 79.355; 2. 32.25; 3. 24.6855.
Bonus Round: 800.28.

page 40
1. 67; 2. 2,170; 3. 46.3.
Bonus Round: 858.3.

page 41
1. $\frac{5}{20}$, $\frac{12}{20}$, $\frac{18}{20}$ or $\frac{1}{4}$, $\frac{3}{5}$, $\frac{9}{10}$; 2. $\frac{9}{24}$, $\frac{12}{24}$, $\frac{20}{24}$ or $\frac{3}{8}$, $\frac{1}{2}$, $\frac{5}{6}$.

page 42
1. right; 2. obtuse; 3. acute; 4. equilateral; 5. isosceles; 6. scalene.
Bonus Round: 50°; 80°; 45°; 32°.

page 43
1. M; 2. A; 3. T; 4. H; 5. I; 6. S; 7. E; 8. A; 9. S; 10. Y.
Bonus Round: MATH IS EASY!

page 44
1. 412; 2. 205; 3. Allenville; 4. 1,776; 5. 444; 6. January; 7. December;
8. January, March; 9. 6 inches; 10. 16 inches; 11. February.

pages 46–47

1. stare; 2. bear; 3. bee; 4. sea; 5. grown; 6. loan; 7. vein; 8. mane;
9. week; 10. peak; 11. steak; 12. break; 13. pane; 14. reign; 15. hour;
16. flour; 17. dye; 18. by; 19. due; 20. ewe; 21. wear; 22. hair; 23. haul;
24. bawl; 25. flue; 26. too; 27. knight; 28. write; 29. won; 30. sun;
31. hoarse; 32. coarse; 33. hear; 34. pier; 35. whole; 36. role; 37. air;
38. pear; 39. pail; 40. sail.
Bonus Round: 41. kernel; 42. minor.

page 48

1. let's; 2. he's; 3. they've; 4. weren't; 5. here's; 6. she's; 7. they're;
8. what's; 9. hasn't; 10. we'll; 11. that's; 12. don't; 13. can't; 14. I'd;
15. they'll; 16. you'll; 17. I've; 18. it's; 19. you're; 20. didn't; 21. she'll;
22. you've; 23. aren't; 24. there's; 25. I'll; 26. isn't; 27. who's;
28. won't; 29. wasn't; 30. she'd; 31. doesn't; 32. he'll.
Bonus Round: 33. have not; 34. you will; 35. we have; 36. could not; 37. they
would (*also,* they had); 38. should not.

page 49

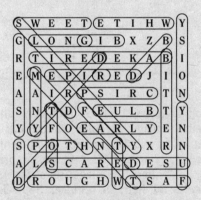

page 50

Answers will vary. Possible answers include:
ate, bait, bate, crate, date, eight, fate, freight, gait, gate, grate, hate,
Kate, late, mate, Nate, pate, plait, plate, rate, skate, slate, state,
straight, strait, trait, wait, weight, abate, await, bookplate,
checkmate, collate, create, dictate, donate, elate, estate, frustrate,
graduate, inflate, inmate, irate, locate, mandate, mismate, mutate,
narrate, ornate, primate, probate, relate, stagnate, vacate,
recapitulate, misappropriate.
Bonus Round: Possible answers include: best, lest, test, dressed, confessed,
nest, pest, guest, jest, west, zest, behest, stressed.

page 51

Answers will vary. Possible answers include:

A. aisle; B. dumb; C. czar; D. Wednesday; E. snore; F. stuff; G. gnu;
H. honest; I. aim; J. San Juan; K. know; L. could; M. mnemonic;
N. hymn; O. rough; P. psychology; Q. acquire; R. Mrs.; S. island;
T. often; U. gauge; V. no answer!; W. write; X. xylophone; Y. gray;
Z. Czechoslovakia. (If you found a V word, excellent!)

page 52

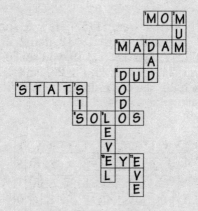

page 53

1. neither; 2. grieve; 3. view; 4. brief; 5. chief; 6. height; 7. friend;
8. believe; 9. conceit; 10. beige; 11. relief; 12. ceiling; 13. mischief;
14. piece; 15. seize; 16. forfeit; 17. protein; 18. ancient; 19. sleight;
20. deceive; 21. receipt; 22. shield; 23. caffeine; 24. priest; 25. thief;
26. reign; 27. field; 28. hygiene; 29. siege; 30. sovereign; 31. glacier;
32. science; 33. species; 34. heir; 35. reindeer; 36. weight; 37. neighbor;
38. cashier; 39. conscience; 40. grief; 41. besiege; 42. sieve; 43. weird;
44. belief; 45. pierce; 46. shriek; 47. frontier; 48. efficient;
49. counterfeit; 50. achieve.

page 54

1. crossroads; 2. six feet underground; 3. touchdown; 4. sign on the
dotted line; 5. square meal; 6. six of one, half a dozen of another;
7. a hole in one; 8. make a mountain out of a molehill; 9. Key West.

page 55

AL; AK; AZ; AR; CA; CO; CT; DE; FL; GA; HI; ID; IL; IN; IA; KS; KY;
LA; ME; MD; MA; MI; MN; MS; MO; MT; NE; NV; NH; NJ; NM; NY;
NC; ND; OH; OK; OR; PA; RI; SC; SD; TN; TX; UT; VT; VA; WA; WV;
WI; WY.
Bonus Round: CZ; DC; GU; PR; VI.

page 56

The Thing in the Lake

On Saturday, July 14, Mom, Dad, and I drove to Sebago Lake.
I was hoping the Morris family and their big bully of a son, Butch,
wouldn't be there waiting for us. Well, Butch was there all right, but
so was something else. Everybody was talking about the monster in
the lake.

"Sheriff Johnson and his deputy stayed up all night watching for
it," said Butch's Aunt Harriet. "They're calling the thing Nessie, after
the Loch Ness Monster. If you ask me, I think it's just a big old carp."

"No child of mine is going to be bait for a lake monster," Mom told
Dad. "I think we should get in the car and go back home to our house
on Pine Street in our safe little town of Pine Bluffs, Massachusetts.
The only monsters there are the dust balls under the bed!"

Just as I was about to complain, I turned for one last look at
Sebago Lake. Guess what I saw waving at me from out in the middle
of the lake? Butch Morris, who else? It was all his idea of one big
joke. The laugh was on him, though, because right behind him
something else was waving, too. It was Nessie, the thing in the lake!
When Butch saw the monster behind him, he swam ashore as fast as
he could.

Butch and his family left and never came back to the lake. As for
Mom, Dad, and me, we stayed and had the best summer ever. Butch's
aunt was right. The "monster" was just a big fish. It's in an aquarium
in Boston now. Thanks to the monster, the really scary thing in the
lake is gone! Bye, Butch. I don't miss you at all!

page 57

1. armchair; downpour; bareback; earthworm; chairperson.
2. teardrop; birthplace; nametag; blackbird; worldwide.
3. scorecard; knapsack; knockout; newspaper; shipwreck.
4. textbook; broomstick; flagpole; suitcase; moonlight.
5. teamwork; streetcar; newborn; chalkboard; playmate.

page 58

who (how)	rat (art)	any (nay)
cat (act)	ore	had
box	car (arc)	ten (net)
and (Dan)	bit	bun (nub)
lip	old	hot
are (ear)	hat	too
put	pat (tap)	now (own)
bus (sub)	bug	fed
mom	tub (but)	dig
two (tow)	gap	bee
nut	for	nap (pan)
oak	far	eye
one	fun	oar
hop	gun (gnu)	zoo
sew	use (sue)	map (Pam)
man	she	bad (dab)

Bonus Round: hand, head, hair, help.

page 59

bat; car; heat; far; ant; Ben; plan; ten; rest; hoe; west; few; pear; ear; pal; sale; law; raw; how; low; ten; end.

page 60

1. hat; 2. painting; 3. swimming; 4. floor; 5. empty; 6. vegetable;
7 taste; 8. enclosing; 9. water; 10. ship; 11. glove; 12. down;
13. eleventh; 14. sled; 15. thermometer.

page 61

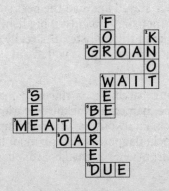

page 62

1. "Did you hear about the three holes in the ground?" Sam asked.

2. "Well, well, well," John answered.

3. Carolyn wondered, "Is anyone going to notice that I got new braces?"

4. "Did you get a new haircut?" John asked Carolyn when she arrived at school the next day.

5. "Look!" shouted my little brother. "The ice cream man forgot to close the freezer door on his truck!"

6. I knew there was only one thing to do. "Hey, ice cream man," I called after him, "you forgot to close the freezer door!"

7. "Some people believe that pepper makes a person sneeze," the teacher said, sprinkling the black grains in her hand. "I myself have never believed that."

8. "Achoo!" she sneezed. "Achoo! Achoo! Achoo!"

page 63

1. 26 = Letters of the Alphabet; 2. 4 and 20 = Blackbirds Baked in a Pie; 3. 9 = Planets in the Solar System; 4. 24 = Hours in a Day; 5. 12 = Months in the Year; 6. 7 = Days in a Week; 7. 4 = Quarts in a Gallon; 8. 13 = Stripes on the U.S. Flag; 9. 52 (53) = Cards in a Deck (with the Joker); 10. 90 = Degrees in a Right Angle; 11. 11 = Players on a Football Team; 12. 3 = Blind Mice "See How They Run."

page 64

Blind as a bat; Dead as a doornail; Cold as ice; Flat as a pancake; Quiet as a mouse; Snug as a bug in a rug; Old as the hills; Sly as a fox; Neat as a pin; Light as a feather; Fit as a fiddle; Busy as a bee; Slow as molasses; Fat as a pig; Proud as a peacock; Nutty as a fruitcake; Sharp as a tack.

page 65

There are no _e's_ in the whole paragraph.

page 66

1. F; 2. T; 3. F; 4. F; 5. T; 6. F; 7. T; 8. F; 9. F; 10. F; 11. F; 12. F; 13. T; 14. F; 15. T; 16. F; 17. F; 18. F; 19. T; 20. T; 21. F; 22. F; 23. T; 24. T; 25. T; 26. F; 27. T; 28. F; 29. F; 30. F; 31. T; 32. F; 33. F.
Bonus Round: 34. F; 35. T.

page 67

1-K; 2-A; 3-N; 4-E; 5-Q; 6-O; 7-B; 8-L; 9-M; 10-P; 11-G; 12-H; 13-I;
14-C; 15-F; 16-J; 17-D.
Bonus Round: Possible answers are: cool, awesome, sweet.

pages 68–69

1. bride-ride; 2. clean-lean; 3. broom-room; 4. drink-rink; 5. price-rice;
6. brake-rake; 7. plane-lane; 8. knight-night; 9. meat-eat; 10. steam-
team; 11. cloud-loud; 12. sore-ore; 13. ghost-host; 14. blame-lame;
15. plate-late; 16. slumber-lumber; 17. claw-law; 18. done-one.

page 70

1. NOthing; 2. kNOb; 3. caNOe; 4. diNOsaur; 5. NOse; 6. miNOrity;
7. hoNOr; 8. NOte; 9. sNOw; 10. miNOr; 11. eNOugh; 12. anNOy;
13. piaNO; 14. NOnsense; 15. canNOt.

page 71

1. cheery Os; 2. fork in the road; 3. low down; 4. much ado about nothing;
5. tall tale; 6. North Pole; 7. tricycle; 8. uptown, downtown; 9. gone south

page 72

1. Corey, tennis, day; 2. he, match; 3. score, point; 4. players, sweat,
faces, sleeves; 5. ground, Corey's feet; 6. ball, baseline, line;
7. He, racquet, ball, contact; 8. Corey, himself, I, match.
Bonus Round: Practice, part, player's game

page 73

1. slow; 2. hot; 3. close; 4. clean; 5. hard; 6. full; 7. big; 8. sad; 9. calm;
10. short; 11. thin; 12. lend; 13. give; 14. sweet; 15. strong; 16. asleep;
17. ceiling; 18. hate; 19. stop; 20. end; 21. life; 22. evil; 23. woman;
24. light; 25. false.

page 74

1. Can you read? 2. I see two or four flowers. 3. Which witch bites and
which one cannot? 4. Do grown bears groan? 5. No one knows whether
or not eight hours passed. 6. Horse herds flew by! 7. One night I heard
some bells ring.

page 75

Caught; daughter; brought; thoughtfully; caught; bought; daughter;
haughtily; taught; naughty; fought; caught; sought; thought; bought.
Bonus Round: taught; slaughter; caught.

page 76

1. 1,001 = Arabian Nights; 2. 18 = Holes on a Golf Course;
3. 200 = Dollars for Passing Go in Monopoly;
4. 5 = Digits in a Zip Code; 5. 10 = Little Indian Boys;
6. 29 = Days in February in a Leap Year; 7. 57 = Heinz Varieties;
8. 2 = Wheels on a Bicycle; 9. 9 = Innings in a Baseball Game;
10. 32 = Degrees Fahrenheit at which Water Freezes;
11. 50 = Stars on the U. S. Flag; 12. 2 = Sides to Every Story.

page 77

G—go, got, goat, gloat ; O—or, oar, boar, board; T—to, ton, tone,
stone; H—ha, ham, harm, charm; H—he, her, hear, heart;
A—at, eat, seat, sweat.

page 78

1. c; 2. d; 3. a; 4. c; 5. d; 6. b; 7. c; 8. b; 9. a; 10. c; 11. d; 12. c; 13. b;
14. a; 15. c; 16. d; 17. c; 18. b; 19. d; 20. b.

page 79

1. S; 2. F; 3. F; 4. F; 5. S; 6. F; 7. F; 8. S; 9. S; 10. S; 11. S; 12. F;
13. S; 14. S; 15. S; 16. F; 17. S; 18. S; 19. S; 20. S.

page 80

1. Yes, I did say I'd meet him on July 25, 1999.
2. I sent a letter to Mr. Coleman's house at 25 Pine Street, Evansville, Virginia.
3. Oh, I wouldn't be too sure about that!
4. Well, we missed the boat.
5. No, we don't plan to move from Boston, Massachusetts, to New York, New York.
6. Ah, you mean you remember the parade on Monday, July 4, 1985?
7. So, do you think your team will win this year?
8. Philadelphia, Pennsylvania, has many sights to see.
9. Yes, we are planning a reunion on December 7, 2002.
10. Oh, who can possibly remember all the names of all the states?
Bonus Round: My grandmother was born February 16, 1938, in Portland, Maine. Oh, how she loves that town!
  "Yes, I think this is the best place in the world!" she says.

page 81

1. dreamed; 2. wrote; 3. thought; 4. worked; 5. read, write, finish;
6. painted, hold; 7. composed; 8. traveled; 9. carried, spoke;
10. wished, fight; 11. made, believe; 12. taught.

page 82

B	R	A	T
R	I	C	H
A	C	H	E
T	H	E	N

G	I	F	T
I	D	E	A
F	E	E	L
T	A	L	L

S	N	O	W
N	I	N	E
O	N	C	E
W	E	E	K

S	N	A	P
N	A	M	E
A	M	E	N
P	E	N	S

page 83

1. bore gone; 2. Mama, I need; 3. color ad on; 4. "Oh, I only;
5. put a ham; 6. miss is sipping; 7. Al ask a; 8. miss our incredible;
9. Mary land; 10. Wade law, a Read law; 11. large or giant;
12. connect, I cut; 13. Ken, tuck your; 14. If Lori dates;
15. ill," I noisily.

page 84

1. deal, dirt, drip, field, files, flies; 2. snow, spoken, sponge, squash,
summer, swing; 3. silly, talent, talk, tall, telephone, under; 4. about,
above, bacon, best, bones, broken; 5. calendar, chance, chapter,
chord, dreary, dresser; 6. odor, open, opera, operation, pencil,
peninsula; 7. mark, match, mound, movie, name, nurse;
8. deduct, defeat, defense, delete, delight, detail.
Bonus Round: All kids learn very well.